Basic Multiplication Tables

S V Morgan

Longman

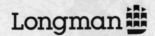

Fill in the answers.
You can look at the 2 × table opposite if you need to.

Multiply:

$3 \times 2 =$ ____

$4 \times 2 =$ ____

$2 \times 2 =$ ____

$5 \times 2 =$ ____

$4 \times 2 =$ ____

$3 \times 2 =$ ____

$5 \times 2 =$ ____

$2 \times 2 =$ ____

$6 \times 2 =$ ____

$5 \times 2 =$ ____

$9 \times 2 =$ ____

$7 \times 2 =$ ____

$4 \times 2 =$ ____

$8 \times 2 =$ ____

$2 \times 2 =$ ____

$7 \times 2 =$ ____

$9 \times 2 =$ ____

$8 \times 2 =$ ____

$5 \times 2 =$ ____

$6 \times 2 =$ ____

$3 \times 2 =$ ____

$7 \times 2 =$ ____

$9 \times 2 =$ ____

$8 \times 2 =$ ____

$4 \times 2 =$ ____

$6 \times 2 =$ ____

$7 \times 2 =$ ____

$8 \times 2 =$ ____

$10 \times 2 =$ ____

$11 \times 2 =$ ____

$12 \times 2 =$ ____

$6 \times 2 =$ ____

$8 \times 2 =$ ____

$7 \times 2 =$ ____

$9 \times 2 =$ ____

$12 \times 2 =$ ____

$10 \times 2 =$ ____

$11 \times 2 =$ ____

$3 \times 2 =$ ____

$4 \times 2 =$ ____

$6 \times 2 =$ ____

$2 \times 2 =$ ____

Now fold this page over on the dotted line and then try these:

Fold here

$6 \times 2 =$ ____

$3 \times 2 =$ ____

$9 \times 2 =$ ____

$5 \times 2 =$ ____

$6 \times 2 =$ ____

$7 \times 2 =$ ____

$4 \times 2 =$ ____

$8 \times 2 =$ ____

$6 \times 2 =$ ____

$7 \times 2 =$ ____

$5 \times 2 =$ ____

$8 \times 2 =$ ____

$2 \times 2 =$ ____

$4 \times 2 =$ ____

$3 \times 2 =$ ____

$7 \times 2 =$ ____

$10 \times 2 =$ ____

$12 \times 2 =$ ____

$11 \times 2 =$ ____

$9 \times 2 =$ ____

Now check your answers with the 2× table.

Score box

How many times did you look?	☐
How many did you get right?	☐

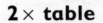

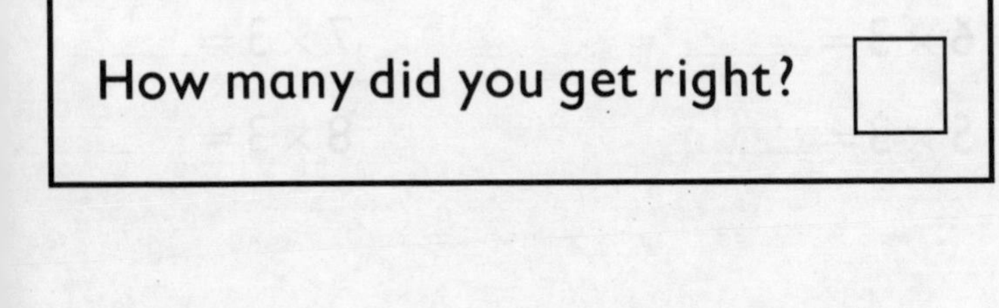

2× table

$1 \times 2 = 2$

$2 \times 2 = 4$

$3 \times 2 = 6$

$4 \times 2 = 8$

$5 \times 2 = 10$

$6 \times 2 = 12$

$7 \times 2 = 14$

$8 \times 2 = 16$

$9 \times 2 = 18$

$10 \times 2 = 20$

$11 \times 2 = 22$

$12 \times 2 = 24$

Fill in the answers.
You can look at the 3 × table opposite if you need to.

Multiply:

$3 \times 3 =$ ______

$2 \times 3 =$ ______

$5 \times 3 =$ ______

$4 \times 3 =$ ______

$2 \times 3 =$ ______

$6 \times 3 =$ ______

$5 \times 3 =$ ______

$3 \times 3 =$ ______

$7 \times 3 =$ ______

$9 \times 3 =$ ______

$2 \times 3 =$ ______

$12 \times 3 =$ ______

$4 \times 3 =$ ______

$8 \times 3 =$ ______

$6 \times 3 =$ ______

$10 \times 3 =$ ______

$6 \times 3 =$ ______

$2 \times 3 =$ ______

$3 \times 3 =$ ______

$5 \times 3 =$ ______

$4 \times 3 =$ ______

$7 \times 3 =$ ______

$11 \times 3 =$ ______

$9 \times 3 =$ ______

$8 \times 3 =$ ______

$10 \times 3 =$ ______

$3 \times 3 =$ ______

$8 \times 3 =$ ______

$6 \times 3 =$ ______

$5 \times 3 =$ ______

$7 \times 3 =$ ______

$10 \times 3 =$ ______

$6 \times 3 =$ ______

$2 \times 3 =$ ______

$8 \times 3 =$ ______

$7 \times 3 =$ ______

$9 \times 3 =$ ______

$3 \times 3 =$ ______

$10 \times 3 =$ ______

$8 \times 3 =$ ______

$5 \times 3 =$ ______

$12 \times 3 =$ ______

$9 \times 3 =$ ______

$7 \times 3 =$ ______

$8 \times 3 =$ ______

Fold this page over on the dotted line.

Try these:

10 × 3 = ____	2 × 3 = ____
3 × 3 = ____	4 × 3 = ____
8 × 3 = ____	12 × 3 = ____
11 × 3 = ____	9 × 3 = ____
2 × 3 = ____	10 × 3 = ____
7 × 3 = ____	8 × 3 = ____
6 × 3 = ____	9 × 3 = ____
5 × 3 = ____	11 × 3 = ____
12 × 3 = ____	7 × 3 = ____
9 × 3 = ____	8 × 3 = ____
4 × 3 = ____	5 × 3 = ____

Now check your answers with the 3 × table.

Score box

How many times did you look? ☐

How many did you get right? ☐

Fold here

3 × table

1 × 3 = 3
2 × 3 = 6
3 × 3 = 9
4 × 3 = 12
5 × 3 = 15
6 × 3 = 18
7 × 3 = 21
8 × 3 = 24
9 × 3 = 27
10 × 3 = 30
11 × 3 = 33
12 × 3 = 36

Complete the last column on page 7.
Check with the tables on pages 3 and 5 if you need to.

Some more practice:

$4 \times 3 =$ ____	$10 \times 3 =$ ____	$9 \times 2 =$ ____
$2 \times 3 =$ ____	$10 \times 2 =$ ____	$8 \times 3 =$ ____
$11 \times 3 =$ ____	$3 \times 3 =$ ____	$9 \times 2 =$ ____
$3 \times 2 =$ ____	$12 \times 2 =$ ____	$7 \times 3 =$ ____
$5 \times 3 =$ ____	$6 \times 3 =$ ____	$8 \times 2 =$ ____
$6 \times 2 =$ ____	$8 \times 2 =$ ____	$9 \times 3 =$ ____
$5 \times 2 =$ ____	$9 \times 2 =$ ____	$6 \times 2 =$ ____
$4 \times 2 =$ ____	$12 \times 3 =$ ____	$11 \times 3 =$ ____
$7 \times 3 =$ ____	$7 \times 2 =$ ____	$7 \times 2 =$ ____
$8 \times 2 =$ ____	$7 \times 3 =$ ____	$8 \times 3 =$ ____
$11 \times 2 =$ ____	$8 \times 3 =$ ____	$9 \times 2 =$ ____
$6 \times 3 =$ ____	$9 \times 3 =$ ____	$6 \times 3 =$ ____
$7 \times 2 =$ ____	$5 \times 2 =$ ____	$12 \times 3 =$ ____
$3 \times 2 =$ ____	$6 \times 2 =$ ____	$4 \times 3 =$ ____
$9 \times 2 =$ ____	$3 \times 2 =$ ____	$2 \times 3 =$ ____

Fold the page over.

Can you get these all right and not look once?

$10 \times 3 =$ ____	$3 \times 2 =$ ____
$8 \times 2 =$ ____	$12 \times 2 =$ ____
$2 \times 3 =$ ____	$4 \times 2 =$ ____
$12 \times 3 =$ ____	$8 \times 3 =$ ____
$7 \times 3 =$ ____	$5 \times 2 =$ ____
$8 \times 2 =$ ____	$7 \times 2 =$ ____
$5 \times 3 =$ ____	$3 \times 3 =$ ____
$5 \times 2 =$ ____	$6 \times 3 =$ ____
$12 \times 2 =$ ____	$9 \times 2 =$ ____
$6 \times 2 =$ ____	$12 \times 3 =$ ____
$6 \times 3 =$ ____	$9 \times 3 =$ ____

Now check your answers.

Score box

How many times did you look?	☐
How many did you get right?	☐

Fold here

Complete

$2 \times$ table

$3 \times 2 =$ ____

$4 \times 2 =$ ____

$5 \times 2 =$ ____

$6 \times 2 =$ ____

$7 \times 2 =$ ____

$8 \times 2 =$ ____

$9 \times 2 =$ ____

$10 \times 2 =$ ____

$11 \times 2 =$ ____

$12 \times 2 =$ ____

$3 \times$ table

$3 \times 3 =$ ____

$4 \times 3 =$ ____

$5 \times 3 =$ ____

$6 \times 3 =$ ____

$7 \times 3 =$ ____

$8 \times 3 =$ ____

$9 \times 3 =$ ____

$10 \times 3 =$ ____

$11 \times 3 =$ ____

$12 \times 3 =$ ____

Multiply:

$3 \times 4 =$ ____

$5 \times 4 =$ ____

$2 \times 4 =$ ____

$4 \times 4 =$ ____

$3 \times 4 =$ ____

$2 \times 4 =$ ____

$3 \times 4 =$ ____

$4 \times 4 =$ ____

$12 \times 4 =$ ____

$2 \times 4 =$ ____

$5 \times 4 =$ ____

$3 \times 4 =$ ____

$4 \times 4 =$ ____

$5 \times 4 =$ ____

$6 \times 4 =$ ____

$3 \times 4 =$ ____

$4 \times 4 =$ ____

$6 \times 4 =$ ____

$5 \times 4 =$ ____

$2 \times 4 =$ ____

$6 \times 4 =$ ____

$3 \times 4 =$ ____

$6 \times 4 =$ ____

$5 \times 4 =$ ____

$11 \times 4 =$ ____

$6 \times 4 =$ ____

$2 \times 4 =$ ____

$3 \times 4 =$ ____

$8 \times 4 =$ ____

$7 \times 4 =$ ____

$8 \times 4 =$ ____

$6 \times 4 =$ ____

$12 \times 4 =$ ____

$7 \times 4 =$ ____

$5 \times 4 =$ ____

$6 \times 4 =$ ____

$9 \times 4 =$ ____

$8 \times 4 =$ ____

$9 \times 4 =$ ____

$7 \times 4 =$ ____

$8 \times 4 =$ ____

$9 \times 4 =$ ____

Fold this page.

Try these.

2 × 4 = ____	3 × 4 = ____
4 × 4 = ____	11 × 4 = ____
3 × 4 = ____	10 × 4 = ____
12 × 4 = ____	8 × 4 = ____
6 × 4 = ____	5 × 4 = ____
5 × 4 = ____	4 × 4 = ____
7 × 4 = ____	7 × 4 = ____
8 × 4 = ____	6 × 4 = ____
11 × 4 = ____	2 × 4 = ____
9 × 4 = ____	12 × 4 = ____
10 × 4 = ____	9 × 4 = ____

Score box

How many times did you look? ☐

How many did you get wrong? ☐

Fold here

4 × table

1 × 4 = 4
2 × 4 = 8
3 × 4 = 12
4 × 4 = 16
5 × 4 = 20
6 × 4 = 24
7 × 4 = 28
8 × 4 = 32
9 × 4 = 36
10 × 4 = 40
11 × 4 = 44
12 × 4 = 48

Multiply:

$5 \times 5 =$ ______

$2 \times 5 =$ ______

$6 \times 5 =$ ______

$3 \times 5 =$ ______

$11 \times 5 =$ ______

$4 \times 5 =$ ______

$8 \times 5 =$ ______

$10 \times 5 =$ ______

$3 \times 5 =$ ______

$2 \times 5 =$ ______

$4 \times 5 =$ ______

$5 \times 5 =$ ______

$3 \times 5 =$ ______

$5 \times 5 =$ ______

$10 \times 5 =$ ______

$8 \times 5 =$ ______

$7 \times 5 =$ ______

$6 \times 5 =$ ______

$9 \times 5 =$ ______

$8 \times 5 =$ ______

$10 \times 5 =$ ______

$9 \times 5 =$ ______

$12 \times 5 =$ ______

$6 \times 5 =$ ______

$7 \times 5 =$ ______

$2 \times 5 =$ ______

$4 \times 5 =$ ______

$8 \times 5 =$ ______

$2 \times 5 =$ ______

$9 \times 5 =$ ______

$12 \times 5 =$ ______

$3 \times 5 =$ ______

$10 \times 5 =$ ______

$4 \times 5 =$ ______

$7 \times 5 =$ ______

$4 \times 5 =$ ______

$6 \times 5 =$ ______

$8 \times 5 =$ ______

$6 \times 5 =$ ______

$7 \times 5 =$ ______

$6 \times 5 =$ ______

$2 \times 5 =$ ______

Fold this page.

Try these:

3 × 5 = ____	8 × 5 = ____
2 × 5 = ____	9 × 5 = ____
11 × 5 = ____	12 × 5 = ____
4 × 5 = ____	7 × 5 = ____
10 × 5 = ____	8 × 5 = ____
12 × 5 = ____	11 × 5 = ____
4 × 5 = ____	7 × 5 = ____
5 × 5 = ____	6 × 5 = ____
10 × 5 = ____	5 × 5 = ____
3 × 5 = ____	9 × 5 = ____
6 × 5 = ____	10 × 5 = ____

Score box

How many times did you look? ☐

How many did you get wrong? ☐

Fold here

5 × table

1 × 5 = 5

2 × 5 = 10

3 × 5 = 15

4 × 5 = 20

5 × 5 = 25

6 × 5 = 30

7 × 5 = 35

8 × 5 = 40

9 × 5 = 45

10 × 5 = 50

11 × 5 = 55

12 × 5 = 60

Complete last column on opposite page.

Try these.

$5 \times 5 =$ ___	$10 \times 3 =$ ___	$2 \times 5 =$ ___
$2 \times 4 =$ ___	$10 \times 2 =$ ___	$6 \times 5 =$ ___
$11 \times 3 =$ ___	$10 \times 5 =$ ___	$6 \times 4 =$ ___
$4 \times 4 =$ ___	$10 \times 4 =$ ___	$5 \times 5 =$ ___
$12 \times 3 =$ ___	$11 \times 4 =$ ___	$8 \times 5 =$ ___
$5 \times 4 =$ ___	$7 \times 2 =$ ___	$6 \times 5 =$ ___
$6 \times 3 =$ ___	$7 \times 3 =$ ___	$11 \times 5 =$ ___
$5 \times 2 =$ ___	$7 \times 4 =$ ___	$7 \times 3 =$ ___
$7 \times 3 =$ ___	$5 \times 5 =$ ___	$7 \times 4 =$ ___
$2 \times 3 =$ ___	$7 \times 5 =$ ___	$7 \times 5 =$ ___
$3 \times 5 =$ ___	$8 \times 5 =$ ___	$9 \times 5 =$ ___
$5 \times 3 =$ ___	$6 \times 4 =$ ___	$12 \times 5 =$ ___
$3 \times 4 =$ ___	$12 \times 4 =$ ___	$3 \times 4 =$ ___
$4 \times 3 =$ ___	$7 \times 3 =$ ___	$9 \times 4 =$ ___
$2 \times 5 =$ ___	$6 \times 3 =$ ___	$10 \times 5 =$ ___

Fold the page over.

Then try these.

8 × 3 = ____	8 × 5 = ____
8 × 4 = ____	9 × 3 = ____
9 × 4 = ____	12 × 4 = ____
9 × 3 = ____	9 × 5 = ____
7 × 4 = ____	8 × 5 = ____
7 × 5 = ____	7 × 3 = ____
10 × 4 = ____	2 × 3 = ____
10 × 3 = ____	4 × 4 = ____
10 × 2 = ____	6 × 4 = ____
12 × 3 = ____	12 × 5 = ____

Score box

How many times did you look? ☐

How many did you get right? ☐

Fold here

Complete first

3 × 3 = ____
4 × 3 = ____
5 × 3 = ____
6 × 3 = ____
7 × 3 = ____
8 × 3 = ____
9 × 3 = ____
10 × 3 = ____
11 × 3 = ____
12 × 3 = ____

4 × 4 = ____
5 × 4 = ____
6 × 4 = ____
7 × 4 = ____
8 × 4 = ____
9 × 4 = ____
10 × 4 = ____
11 × 4 = ____
12 × 4 = ____

5 × 5 = ____
6 × 5 = ____
7 × 5 = ____
8 × 5 = ____
9 × 5 = ____
10 × 5 = ____
11 × 5 = ____
12 × 5 = ____

Multiply:

$3 \times 6 =$ _____

$2 \times 6 =$ _____

$4 \times 6 =$ _____

$6 \times 6 =$ _____

$2 \times 6 =$ _____

$4 \times 6 =$ _____

$5 \times 6 =$ _____

$3 \times 6 =$ _____

$2 \times 6 =$ _____

$4 \times 6 =$ _____

$3 \times 6 =$ _____

$5 \times 6 =$ _____

$4 \times 6 =$ _____

$12 \times 6 =$ _____

$6 \times 6 =$ _____

$7 \times 6 =$ _____

$6 \times 6 =$ _____

$5 \times 6 =$ _____

$7 \times 6 =$ _____

$6 \times 6 =$ _____

$5 \times 6 =$ _____

$3 \times 6 =$ _____

$6 \times 6 =$ _____

$7 \times 6 =$ _____

$4 \times 6 =$ _____

$6 \times 6 =$ _____

$7 \times 6 =$ _____

$11 \times 6 =$ _____

$2 \times 6 =$ _____

$6 \times 6 =$ _____

$5 \times 6 =$ _____

$7 \times 6 =$ _____

$9 \times 6 =$ _____

$10 \times 6 =$ _____

$9 \times 6 =$ _____

$12 \times 6 =$ _____

$8 \times 6 =$ _____

$6 \times 6 =$ _____

$9 \times 6 =$ _____

$2 \times 6 =$ _____

$7 \times 6 =$ _____

$8 \times 6 =$ _____

Fold this page over.

Try these.

$7 \times 6 =$ _____

$8 \times 6 =$ _____

$2 \times 6 =$ _____

$4 \times 6 =$ _____

$3 \times 6 =$ _____

$5 \times 6 =$ _____

$10 \times 6 =$ _____

$4 \times 6 =$ _____

$9 \times 6 =$ _____

$8 \times 6 =$ _____

$12 \times 6 =$ _____

$3 \times 6 =$ _____

$4 \times 6 =$ _____

$10 \times 6 =$ _____

$9 \times 6 =$ _____

$5 \times 6 =$ _____

$7 \times 6 =$ _____

$6 \times 6 =$ _____

$8 \times 6 =$ _____

$12 \times 6 =$ _____

$4 \times 6 =$ _____

$9 \times 6 =$ _____

Score box

How many times did you look? ☐

How many did you get right? ☐

Fold here

6 × table

$1 \times 6 = 6$

$2 \times 6 = 12$

$3 \times 6 = 18$

$4 \times 6 = 24$

$5 \times 6 = 30$

$6 \times 6 = 36$

$7 \times 6 = 42$

$8 \times 6 = 48$

$9 \times 6 = 54$

$10 \times 6 = 60$

$11 \times 6 = 66$

$12 \times 6 = 72$

Fill in the answers and missing numbers.

$3 \times 7 =$ ____

$2 \times 7 =$ ____

$1 \times 7 =$ ____

$7 \times 7 =$ ____

$9 \times 7 =$ ____

$4 \times 7 =$ ____

$10 \times 7 =$ ____

$11 \times 7 =$ ____

$5 \times 7 =$ ____

$6 \times 7 =$ ____

$12 \times 7 =$ ____

$8 \times 7 =$ ____

$9 \times 7 =$ ____

$4 \times 7 =$ ____

$5 \times 7 =$ ____

$11 \times 7 =$ ____

$12 \times 7 =$ ____

$4 \times 7 =$ ____

$8 \times 7 =$ ____

$2 \times 7 =$ ____

$3 \times 7 =$ ____

$9 \times 7 =$ ____

$7 \times 7 =$ ____

$5 \times 7 =$ ____

$1 \times 7 =$ ____

$10 \times 7 =$ ____

$6 \times 7 =$ ____

$11 \times 7 =$ ____

____ $\times 7 = 14$

____ $\times 7 = 28$

____ $\times 7 = 63$

____ $\times 7 = 70$

____ $\times 7 = 77$

____ $\times 7 = 7$

____ $\times 7 = 42$

____ $\times 7 = 35$

____ $\times 7 = 21$

____ $\times 7 = 56$

____ $\times 7 = 49$

____ $\times 7 = 35$

____ $\times 7 = 84$

____ $\times 7 = 63$

Fold the page over.

$10 \times 7 =$ ____	____ $\times 7 = 49$
$11 \times 7 =$ ____	____ $\times 7 = 14$
$9 \times 7 =$ ____	____ $\times 7 = 63$
$12 \times 7 =$ ____	____ $\times 7 = 56$
$6 \times 7 =$ ____	____ $\times 7 = 35$
$3 \times 7 =$ ____	____ $\times 7 = 84$
$2 \times 7 =$ ____	____ $\times 7 = 77$
$4 \times 7 =$ ____	____ $\times 7 = 70$
$8 \times 7 =$ ____	____ $\times 7 = 28$
$5 \times 7 =$ ____	____ $\times 7 = 42$

Score box

How many times did you look?	☐
How many did you get right?	☐

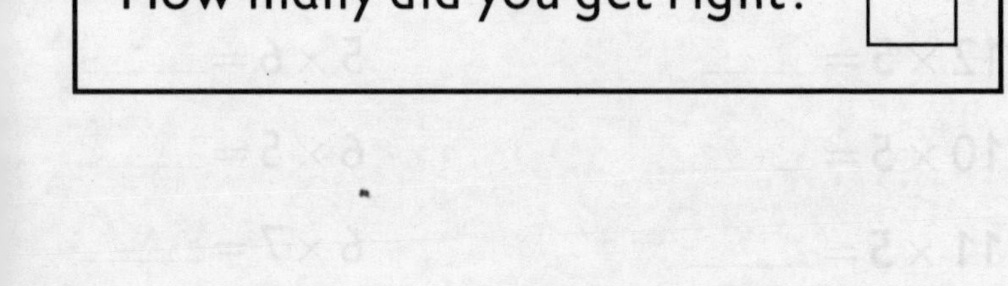

Fold here

$1 \times 7 = 7$

$2 \times 7 = 14$

$3 \times 7 = 21$

$4 \times 7 = 28$

$5 \times 7 = 35$

$6 \times 7 = 42$

$7 \times 7 = 49$

$8 \times 7 = 56$

$9 \times 7 = 63$

$10 \times 7 = 70$

$11 \times 7 = 77$

$12 \times 7 = 84$

Complete the last column on page 19.

Multiply:

$7 \times 7 =$ ______

$8 \times 7 =$ ______

$8 \times 6 =$ ______

$8 \times 5 =$ ______

$6 \times 6 =$ ______

$6 \times 7 =$ ______

$6 \times 8 =$ ______

$5 \times 5 =$ ______

$5 \times 6 =$ ______

$5 \times 7 =$ ______

$4 \times 7 =$ ______

$4 \times 6 =$ ______

$4 \times 5 =$ ______

$4 \times 7 =$ ______

$3 \times 7 =$ ______

$3 \times 6 =$ ______

$3 \times 5 =$ ______

$7 \times 3 =$ ______

$7 \times 2 =$ ______

$7 \times 7 =$ ______

$12 \times 7 =$ ______

$10 \times 7 =$ ______

$11 \times 7 =$ ______

$12 \times 6 =$ ______

$11 \times 6 =$ ______

$10 \times 6 =$ ______

$12 \times 5 =$ ______

$11 \times 5 =$ ______

$3 \times 5 =$ ______

$2 \times 5 =$ ______

$4 \times 5 =$ ______

$12 \times 5 =$ ______

$10 \times 5 =$ ______

$11 \times 5 =$ ______

$9 \times 5 =$ ______

$5 \times 5 =$ ______

$7 \times 5 =$ ______

$6 \times 5 =$ ______

$8 \times 5 =$ ______

$12 \times 7 =$ ______

$12 \times 6 =$ ______

$11 \times 7 =$ ______

$11 \times 6 =$ ______

$9 \times 7 =$ ______

$9 \times 6 =$ ______

$8 \times 6 =$ ______

$8 \times 7 =$ ______

$7 \times 8 =$ ______

$5 \times 6 =$ ______

$6 \times 5 =$ ______

$6 \times 7 =$ ______

Fold this page over and try these.

12 × ___ = 60

12 × ___ = 84

12 × ___ = 72

9 × ___ = 54

___ × 9 = 45

8 × ___ = 56

___ × 7 = 42

7 × ___ = 56

___ × 6 = 42

9 × ___ = 63

6 × ___ = 36

5 × ___ = 25

7 × ___ = 49

6 × ___ = 18

___ × 7 = 21

___ × 6 = 24

___ × 5 = 15

___ × 7 = 28

___ × 6 = 30

___ × 5 = 20

Score box

How many times did you look? ☐

How many did you get right? ☐

Fold here

Do these first.

5 × 5 = ___

6 × 5 = ___

7 × 5 = ___

8 × 5 = ___

9 × 5 = ___

10 × 5 = ___

11 × 5 = ___

12 × 5 = ___

6 × 6 = ___

7 × 6 = ___

8 × 6 = ___

9 × 6 = ___

10 × 6 = ___

11 × 6 = ___

12 × 6 = ___

7 × 7 = ___

8 × 7 = ___

9 × 7 = ___

10 × 7 = ___

11 × 7 = ___

12 × 7 = ___

Fill in the answers.

$2 \times 8 =$ ______

$6 \times 8 =$ ______

$3 \times 8 =$ ______

$7 \times 8 =$ ______

$5 \times 8 =$ ______

$6 \times 8 =$ ______

$2 \times 8 =$ ______

$3 \times 8 =$ ______

$7 \times 8 =$ ______

$4 \times 8 =$ ______

$2 \times 8 =$ ______

$6 \times 8 =$ ______

$11 \times 8 =$ ______

$5 \times 8 =$ ______

$7 \times 8 =$ ______

$3 \times 8 =$ ______

$2 \times 8 =$ ______

$5 \times 8 =$ ______

$8 \times 8 =$ ______

$3 \times 8 =$ ______

$6 \times 8 =$ ______

$2 \times 8 =$ ______

$7 \times 8 =$ ______

$4 \times 8 =$ ______

$5 \times 8 =$ ______

$12 \times 8 =$ ______

$3 \times 8 =$ ______

$9 \times 8 =$ ______

$7 \times 8 =$ ______

$8 \times 8 =$ ______

$6 \times 8 =$ ______

$2 \times 8 =$ ______

$9 \times 8 =$ ______

$7 \times 8 =$ ______

$6 \times 8 =$ ______

$5 \times 8 =$ ______

$11 \times 8 =$ ______

$3 \times 8 =$ ______

$4 \times 8 =$ ______

$10 \times 8 =$ ______

$6 \times 8 =$ ______

$9 \times 8 =$ ______

$7 \times 8 =$ ______

$10 \times 8 =$ ______

$4 \times 8 =$ ______

$10 \times 8 =$ ______

$3 \times 8 =$ ______

$12 \times 8 =$ ______

$9 \times 8 =$ ______

$8 \times 8 =$ ______

$7 \times 8 =$ ______

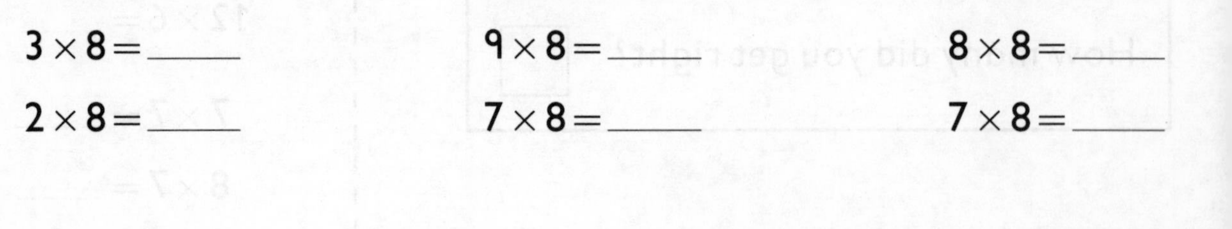

Fold this page over.

Try these.

12 × 8 = ____

10 × 8 = ____

11 × 8 = ____

6 × 8 = ____

5 × 8 = ____

8 × 8 = ____

4 × 8 = ____

3 × 8 = ____

7 × 8 = ____

9 × 8 = ____

Tricky ones

9 × 8 = ____

8 × 8 = ____

7 × 7 = ____

7 × 8 = ____

6 × 7 = ____

8 × 6 = ____

8 × 7 = ____

12 × 8 = ____

9 × 8 = ____

8 × 8 = ____

Score box

How many tricky ones did you get right? ☐

Fold here

8 × table

1 × 8 = 8

2 × 8 = 16

3 × 8 = 24

4 × 8 = 32

5 × 8 = 40

6 × 8 = 48

7 × 8 = 56

8 × 8 = 64

9 × 8 = 72

10 × 8 = 80

11 × 8 = 88

12 × 8 = 96

Fill in the answers.

2 × 9 = ____

9 × 3 = ____

4 × 9 = ____

3 × 9 = ____

9 × 2 = ____

9 × 4 = ____

9 × ____ = 18

____ × 9 = 27

2 × ____ = 18

9 × ____ = 36

____ × 5 = 45

9 × 3 = ____

4 × 9 = ____

12 × 9 = ____

5 × 9 = ____

9 × 6 = ____

____ × 9 = 36

____ × 9 = 54

9 × 6 = ____

7 × 9 = ____

5 × 9 = ____

9 × 6 = ____

9 × 7 = ____

____ × 9 = 63

6 × ____ = 54

9 × 6 = ____

9 × ____ = 45

10 × 9 = ____

2 × 9 = ____

3 × 9 = ____

9 × 4 = ____

7 × 9 = ____

12 × 9 = ____

10 × 9 = ____

11 × 9 = ____

9 × 2 = ____

9 × 3 = ____

____ × 9 = 27

3 × ____ = 27

____ × 9 = 99

____ × 9 = 90

12 × ____ = 108

8 × 9 = ____

9 × 6 = ____

7 × 9 = ____

9 × 7 = ____

6 × 9 = ____

9 × 8 = ____

____ × 9 = 54

____ × 6 = 54

____ × 8 = 72

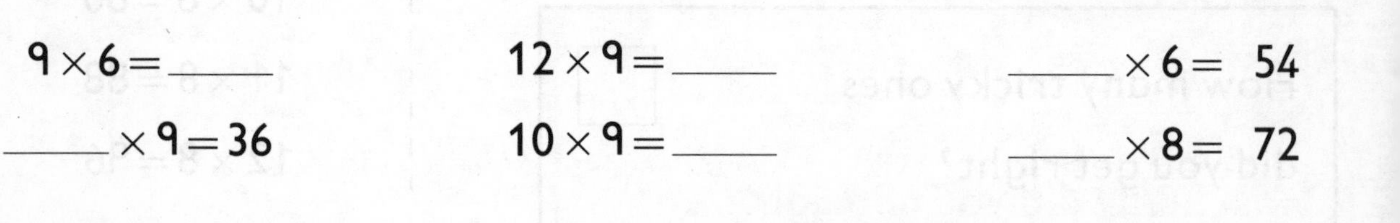

Fold this page over.

Then try these.

$9 \times 9 =$ ____

$3 \times 9 =$ ____

____ $\times 9 = 18$

____ $\times 9 = 27$

$12 \times 9 =$ ____

$11 \times 9 =$ ____

____ $\times 9 = 108$

____ $\times 9 = 99$

$4 \times 9 =$ ____

$5 \times 9 =$ ____

$6 \times 9 =$ ____

$7 \times 9 =$ ____

$8 \times 9 =$ ____

____ $\times 9 = 63$

____ $\times 9 = 36$

____ $\times 9 = 45$

____ $\times 9 = 27$

____ $\times 9 = 54$

$9 \times 4 =$ ____

$9 \times 8 =$ ____

Score box

How many times did you look?	☐
How many did you get right?	☐

Fold here

9 × table

$1 \times 9 = 9$

$2 \times 9 = 18$

$3 \times 9 = 27$

$4 \times 9 = 36$

$5 \times 9 = 45$

$6 \times 9 = 54$

$7 \times 9 = 63$

$8 \times 9 = 72$

$9 \times 9 = 81$

$10 \times 9 = 90$

$11 \times 9 = 99$

$12 \times 9 = 108$

Fill in the answers.

You can look at the 10 × and 11 × tables if you need to.

3 × 10 = ____
5 × 10 = ____
4 × 10 = ____
11 × 10 = ____
12 × 10 = ____
8 × 10 = ____
9 × 10 = ____
2 × 10 = ____
7 × 10 = ____
4 × 10 = ____
6 × 10 = ____
12 × 10 = ____
9 × 10 = ____
7 × 10 = ____
11 × 10 = ____
10 × 10 = ____
6 × 10 = ____

4 × 10 = ____
5 × 10 = ____
3 × 10 = ____
2 × 10 = ____
9 × 10 = ____
8 × 10 = ____
5 × 10 = ____
10 × 5 = ____
10 × 4 = ____
10 × 6 = ____
10 × 3 = ____
10 × 2 = ____
10 × 11 = ____
10 × 9 = ____
10 × 12 = ____
10 × 7 = ____
10 × 8 = ____

____ × 10 = 50
____ × 10 = 90
____ × 10 = 110
____ × 11 = 44
____ × 11 = 55
____ × 11 = 66
____ × 11 = 77
____ × 11 = 99
____ × 11 = 33
____ × 10 = 40
____ × 10 = 120
____ × 11 = 110
____ × 11 = 132
____ × 10 = 100
____ × 11 = 121
____ × 10 = 110
____ × 11 = 22

Fold the page.

Try these.

4 × 11 = ____	11 × 11 = ____
6 × 11 = ____	____ × 11 = 99
8 × 11 = ____	11 × ____ = 110
10 × 11 = ____	12 × ____ = 132
12 × 11 = ____	____ × 11 = 66
5 × 11 = ____	____ × 11 = 55
7 × 11 = ____	11 × ____ = 33
9 × 11 = ____	11 × ____ = 77
11 × 10 = ____	11 × ____ = 22
11 × 12 = ____	____ × 11 = 44

Score box

How many times did you look? ☐

How many did you get right? ☐

Fold here

10 × table

1 × 10 = 10
2 × 10 = 20
3 × 10 = 30
4 × 10 = 40
5 × 10 = 50
6 × 10 = 60
7 × 10 = 70
8 × 10 = 80
9 × 10 = 90
10 × 10 = 100
11 × 10 = 110
12 × 10 = 120

11 × table

1 × 11 = 11
2 × 11 = 22
3 × 11 = 33
4 × 11 = 44
5 × 11 = 55
6 × 11 = 66
7 × 11 = 77
8 × 11 = 88
9 × 11 = 99
10 × 11 = 110
11 × 11 = 121
12 × 11 = 132

Complete the right-hand column on page 27 first.

Now try these.

9 × 9 = ____

8 × 9 = ____

9 × 8 = ____

____ × 9 = 81

9 × ____ = 72

3 × 9 = ____

8 × 9 = ____

____ × 9 = 27

8 × ____ = 72

2 × 9 = ____

____ × 9 = 18

____ × 9 = 81

4 × 8 = ____

3 × 8 = ____

3 × 9 = ____

4 × 9 = ____

5 × 8 = ____

9 × 5 = ____

5 × 9 = ____

7 × 8 = ____

9 × 7 = ____

____ × 8 = 56

____ × 8 = 64

12 × 9 = ____

12 × 11 = ____

11 × 10 = ____

8 × 8 = ____

6 × 8 = ____

6 × 9 = ____

____ × 8 = 48

____ × 8 = 72

____ × 9 = 72

____ × 9 = 36

____ × 9 = 90

____ × 9 = 45

____ × 11 = 121

5 × 8 = ____

4 × 8 = ____

3 × 8 = ____

8 × 8 = ____

8 × 7 = ____

8 × 6 = ____

8 × 5 = ____

8 × 4 = ____

8 × 3 = ____

8 × 2 = ____

9 × 7 = ____

9 × 6 = ____

9 × 5 = ____

9 × 4 = ____

9 × 3 = ____

Fold this page over.

Then try these.

12 × 11 = ____
11 × 11 = ____
10 × 11 = ____
2 × 10 = ____
12 × 10 = ____
3 × 11 = ____
5 × 11 = ____
7 × 11 = ____
9 × 11 = ____
11 × 10 = ____

4 × 10 = ____
6 × 10 = ____
8 × 10 = ____
8 × 7 = ____
9 × 8 = ____
7 × 8 = ____
8 × 9 = ____
10 × 10 = ____
12 × 11 = ____
10 × 11 = ____

Score box

How many did you get right? ☐

Fold here

Complete first.

8 × 8 = ____
9 × 8 = ____
10 × 8 = ____
11 × 8 = ____
12 × 8 = ____

9 × 9 = ____
10 × 9 = ____
11 × 9 = ____
12 × 9 = ____

10 × 10 = ____
11 × 10 = ____
12 × 10 = ____

10 × 11 = ____
11 × 11 = ____
12 × 11 = ____

4 × 12 = ____
2 × 12 = ____
5 × 12 = ____
3 × 12 = ____
6 × 12 = ____
8 × 12 = ____
7 × 12 = ____
12 × 12 = ____
10 × 12 = ____
4 × 12 = ____
11 × 12 = ____
9 × 12 = ____
12 × 12 = ____
12 × 9 = ____
12 × 11 = ____
12 × 4 = ____
12 × 10 = ____

12 × 6 = ____
12 × 8 = ____
12 × 3 = ____
12 × 5 = ____
12 × 2 = ____
12 × 7 = ____
12 × 12 = ____
12 × 5 = ____
12 × ____ = 120
12 × ____ = 144
12 × ____ = 72
12 × ____ = 96
12 × ____ = 84
12 × ____ = 12
12 × ____ = 36
12 × ____ = 24
12 × ____ = 0

12 × ____ = 48
12 × ____ = 60
12 × ____ = 96
12 × ____ = 132
____ × 12 = 72
6 × ____ = 72
____ × 12 = 60
12 × ____ = 60
____ × 12 = 144
____ × 12 = 96
12 × ____ = 12
____ × 3 = 36
12 × ____ = 84
____ × 11 = 132
12 × ____ = 108
____ × 12 = 0
12 × ____ = 48

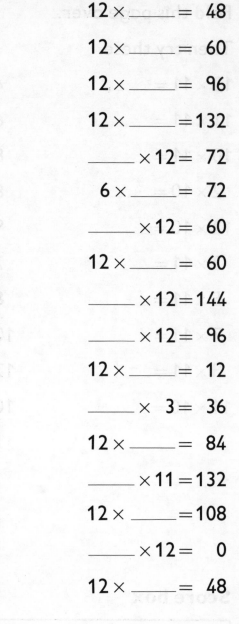

Fold the paper over.

Do these sums.

12 × 11 = ____	12 × ____ = 144
12 × 9 = ____	12 × ____ = 108
12 × 7 = ____	12 × ____ = 72
12 × 5 = ____	12 × ____ = 36
12 × 3 = ____	12 × ____ = 12
12 × 4 = ____	12 × ____ = 48
12 × 6 = ____	12 × ____ = 24
12 × 8 = ____	12 × ____ = 120
12 × 10 = ____	12 × ____ = 60
12 × 12 = ____	12 × ____ = 132

Can you remember these?

7 × 8 = ____	8 × 9 = ____
6 × 7 = ____	9 × 11 = ____
9 × 6 = ____	11 × 11 = ____

Fold here

12 × table

1 × 12 = 12
2 × 12 = 24
3 × 12 = 36
4 × 12 = 48
5 × 12 = 60
6 × 12 = 72
7 × 12 = 84
8 × 12 = 96
9 × 12 = 108
10 × 12 = 120
11 × 12 = 132
12 × 12 = 144

If you can get all these right, you are an expert!

6 × 5 = ____
7 × 3 = ____
8 × 8 = ____
9 × 7 = ____
5 × 2 = ____
7 × 3 = ____
7 × 7 = ____
6 × 4 = ____
5 × 3 = ____
4 × 2 = ____
7 × 8 = ____
9 × 2 = ____
12 × 11 = ____
2 × 2 = ____
2 × 6 = ____
3 × 3 = ____
3 × 2 = ____

5 × 4 = ____
8 × 5 = ____
8 × 2 = ____
10 × 5 = ____
5 × 6 = ____
9 × 5 = ____
4 × 8 = ____
9 × 3 = ____
7 × 2 = ____
10 × 11 = ____
9 × 9 = ____
3 × 8 = ____
10 × 4 = ____
6 × 6 = ____
6 × 8 = ____
11 × 11 = ____
7 × 6 = ____

5 × 3 = ____
2 × 9 = ____
10 × 7 = ____
9 × 9 = ____
9 × 3 = ____
2 × 4 = ____
10 × 2 = ____
4 × 3 = ____
3 × 6 = ____
7 × 4 = ____
5 × 7 = ____
9 × 6 = ____
2 × 5 = ____
6 × 7 = ____
8 × 8 = ____
5 × 5 = ____
11 × 12 = ____

Now try these.

10 × 3 = ____

4 × 4 = ____

9 × 4 = ____

5 × 5 = ____

7 × 6 = ____

10 × 6 = ____

9 × 9 = ____

11 × 11 = ____

7 × 7 = ____

5 × 7 = ____

6 × 7 = ____

7 × 5 = ____

7 × 6 = ____

8 × 7 = ____

7 × 8 = ____

7 × 9 = ____

9 × 8 = ____

8 × 9 = ____

7 × 9 = ____

11 × 12 = ____

7 × 8 = ____

8 × 9 = ____

8 × 8 = ____

6 × ____ = 42

7 × ____ = 49

3 × ____ = 24

8 × ____ = 64

9 × ____ = 72

6 × ____ = 54

8 × ____ = 72

9 × ____ = 54

7 × ____ = 56

9 × ____ = 81

9 × ____ = 18

8 × ____ = 24

6 × ____ = 48

11 × 11 = ____

5 × ____ = 40

7 × ____ = 35

6 × ____ = 54

9 × ____ = 45

9 × ____ = 36

7 × ____ = 63

3 × ____ = 27

8 × ____ = 72

6 × ____ = 12

3 × ____ = 21

8 × ____ = 64

5 × ____ = 30

9 × ____ = 63

12 × 12 = ____

1 × 2 = 2	1 × 3 = 3	1 × 4 = 4	1 × 5 = 5
2 × 2 = 4	2 × 3 = 6	2 × 4 = 8	2 × 5 = 10
3 × 2 = 6	3 × 3 = 9	3 × 4 = 12	3 × 5 = 15
4 × 2 = 8	4 × 3 = 12	4 × 4 = 16	4 × 5 = 20
5 × 2 = 10	5 × 3 = 15	5 × 4 = 20	5 × 5 = 25
6 × 2 = 12	6 × 3 = 18	6 × 4 = 24	6 × 5 = 30
7 × 2 = 14	7 × 3 = 21	7 × 4 = 28	7 × 5 = 35
8 × 2 = 16	8 × 3 = 24	8 × 4 = 32	8 × 5 = 40
9 × 2 = 18	9 × 3 = 27	9 × 4 = 36	9 × 5 = 45
10 × 2 = 20	10 × 3 = 30	10 × 4 = 40	10 × 5 = 50
11 × 2 = 22	11 × 3 = 33	11 × 4 = 44	11 × 5 = 55
12 × 2 = 24	12 × 3 = 36	12 × 4 = 48	12 × 5 = 60

1 × 6 = 6	1 × 7 = 7	1 × 8 = 8	1 × 9 = 9
2 × 6 = 12	2 × 7 = 14	2 × 8 = 16	2 × 9 = 18
3 × 6 = 18	3 × 7 = 21	3 × 8 = 24	3 × 9 = 27
4 × 6 = 24	4 × 7 = 28	4 × 8 = 32	4 × 9 = 36
5 × 6 = 30	5 × 7 = 35	5 × 8 = 40	5 × 9 = 45
6 × 6 = 36	6 × 7 = 42	6 × 8 = 48	6 × 9 = 54
7 × 6 = 42	7 × 7 = 49	7 × 8 = 56	7 × 9 = 63
8 × 6 = 48	8 × 7 = 56	8 × 8 = 64	8 × 9 = 72
9 × 6 = 54	9 × 7 = 63	9 × 8 = 72	9 × 9 = 81
10 × 6 = 60	10 × 7 = 70	10 × 8 = 80	10 × 9 = 90
11 × 6 = 66	11 × 7 = 77	11 × 8 = 88	11 × 9 = 99
12 × 6 = 72	12 × 7 = 84	12 × 8 = 96	12 × 9 = 108

1 × 10 = 10	1 × 11 = 11	1 × 12 = 12
2 × 10 = 20	2 × 11 = 22	2 × 12 = 24
3 × 10 = 30	3 × 11 = 33	3 × 12 = 36
4 × 10 = 40	4 × 11 = 44	4 × 12 = 48
5 × 10 = 50	5 × 11 = 55	5 × 12 = 60
6 × 10 = 60	6 × 11 = 66	6 × 12 = 72
7 × 10 = 70	7 × 11 = 77	7 × 12 = 84
8 × 10 = 80	8 × 11 = 88	8 × 12 = 96
9 × 10 = 90	9 × 11 = 99	9 × 12 = 108
10 × 10 = 100	10 × 11 = 110	10 × 12 = 120
11 × 10 = 110	11 × 11 = 121	11 × 12 = 132
12 × 10 = 120	12 × 11 = 132	12 × 12 = 144